{LINKIN PARK} METE

Transcribed by Bill LaFleur, except "Somewhere I Belong," transcribed by Andy Aledort

Project Managers: Jeannette DeLisa and Aaron Stang
Music Editor: Colgan Bryan
Book Art Layout: Joe Klucar
Album Art: © 2003 Warner Bros. Records Inc.
Photography: James R. Minchin III
Spray Paint Can Close-up Photos: Nick Spanos

Exclusive distributors:
Music Sales Limited
Distribution Centre, Newmarket Road,
Bury St Edmunds Suffolk IP33 3YB, England.
Music Sales Pty Limited
120 Rothschild Avenue, Rosebery, NSW 2018, Australia.

Order No. AM978912
ISBN 1-84449-304-0
This book © Copyright 2003 by Wise Publications.

EORA

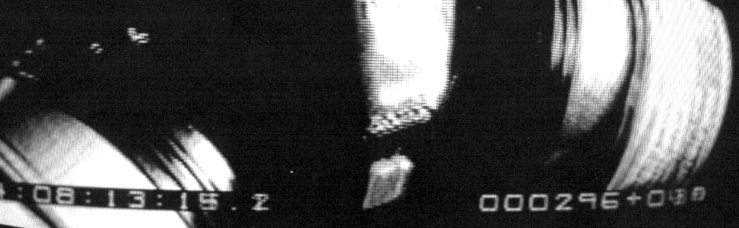

DON'T STAY

By LINKIN PARK

All gtrs. in Drop D, down 1 1/2 steps:

⑥ = B ③ = E
⑤ = F♯ ② = G♯
④ = B ① = C♯

Moderate rock ♩ = 86

Intro:

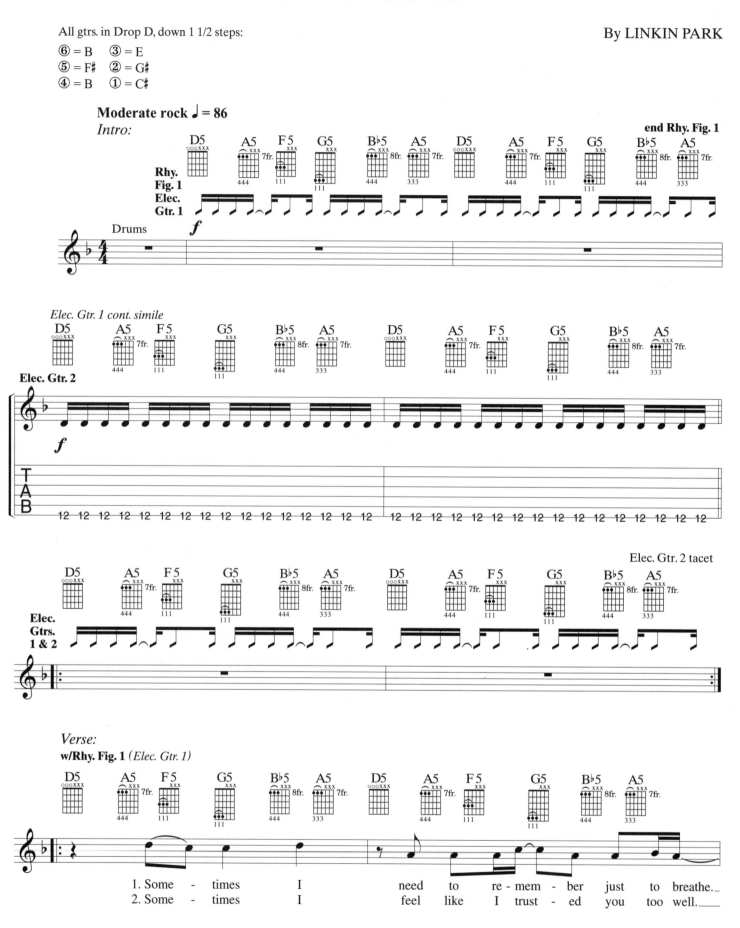

1. Some - times   I   need to re - mem - ber just to breathe._
2. Some - times   I   feel like I trust - ed you too well.___

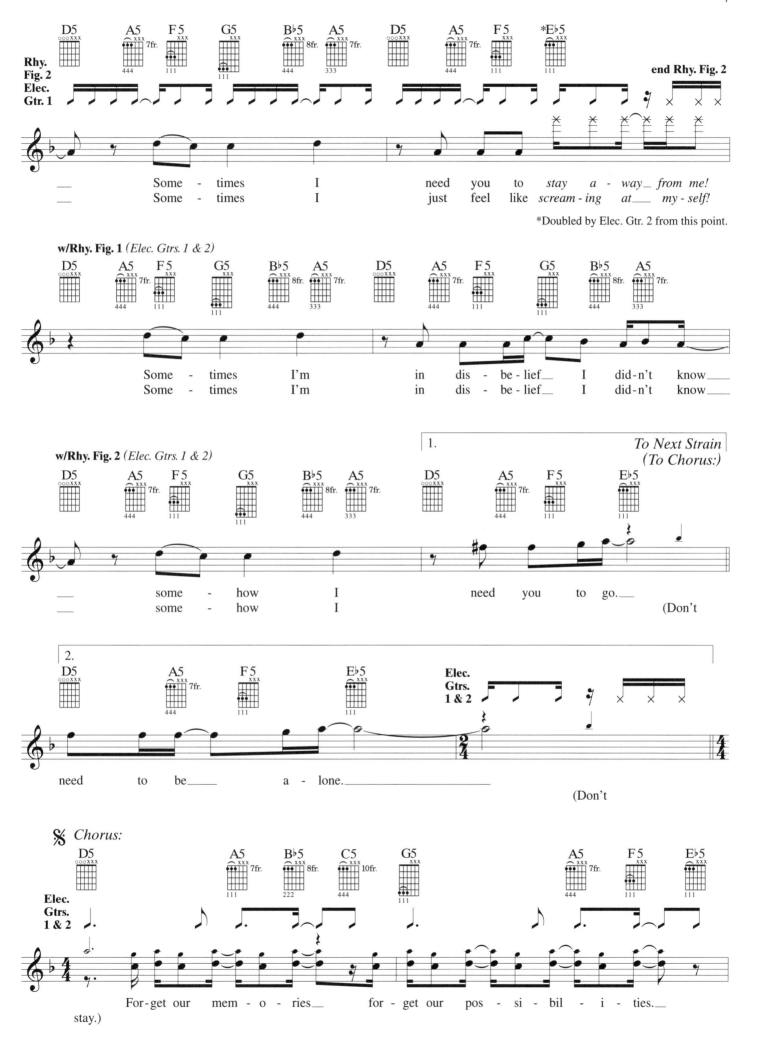

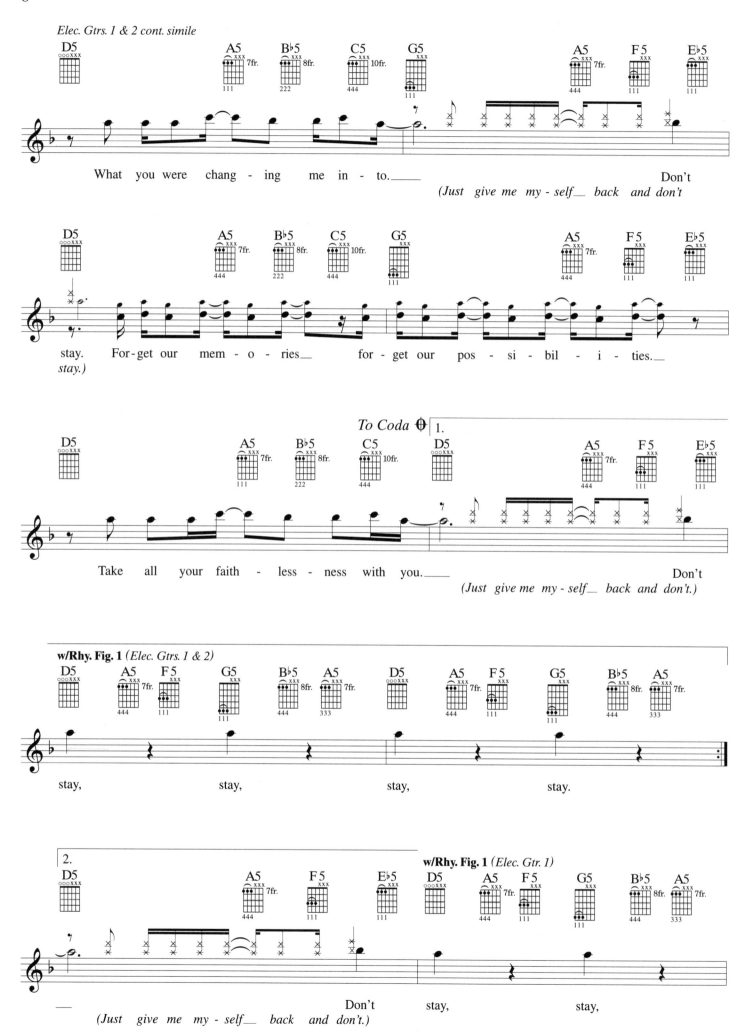

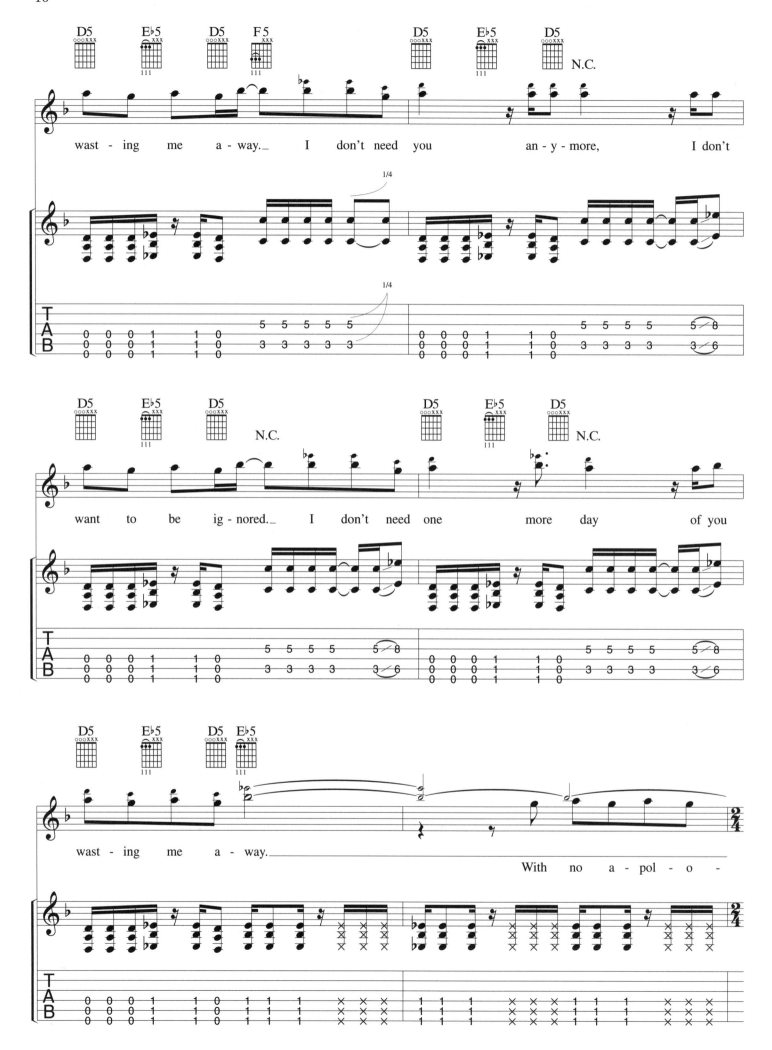

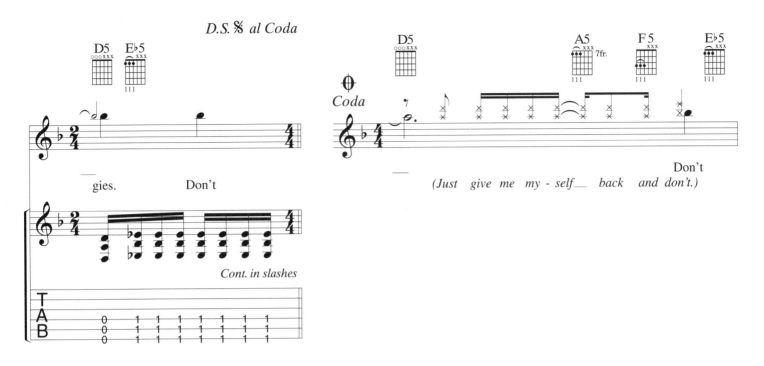

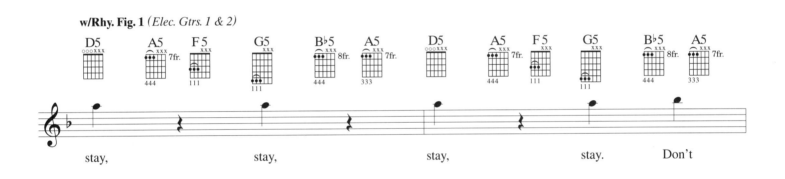

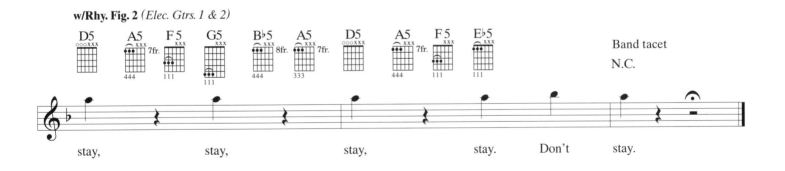

SOMEWHERE I BELONG

By LINKIN PARK

Tune down 1/2 step:
⑥ = E♭   ③ = G♭
⑤ = A♭   ② = B♭
④ = D♭   ① = E♭

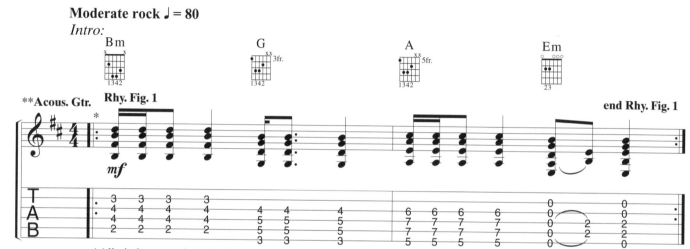

*All pitches sound one half step lower than written (key of B♭ minor).
**Acous. Gtr. part is digitally processed using Pro Tools, creating a "backwards" effect.

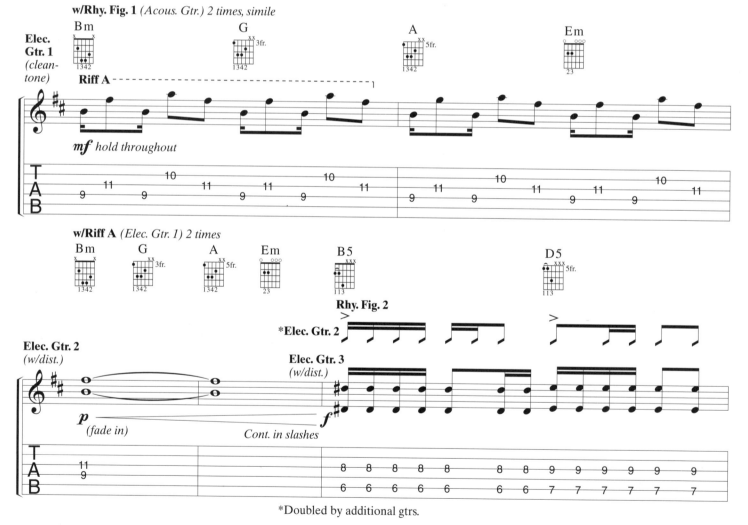

*Doubled by additional gtrs.

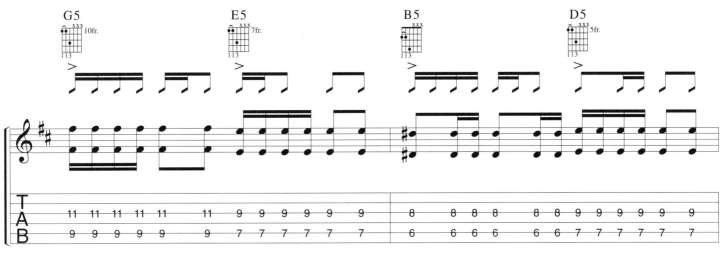

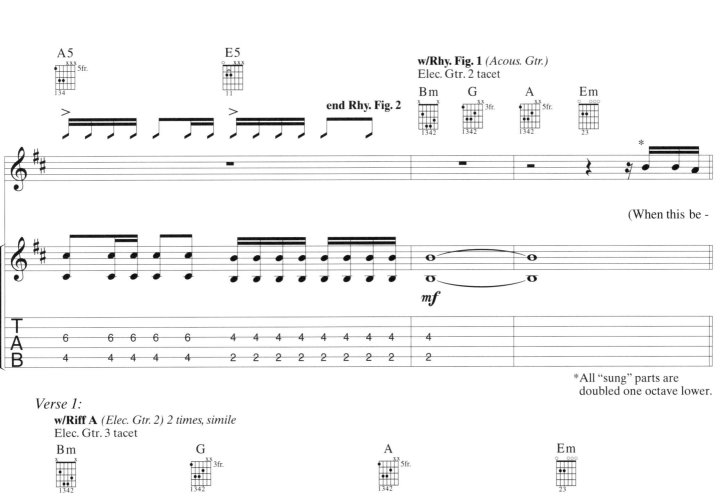

*All "sung" parts are
doubled one octave lower.

Verse 1:

w/Riff A *(Elec. Gtr. 2) 2 times, simile*
Elec. Gtr. 3 tacet

I had noth-in' to say,_ and I'd get lost in the noth-ing-ness in-side of me._ (I was con-

gan)

Acous. Gtr.

w/Rhy. Fig. 1 *(Acous. Gtr.) 3 times*

Bm   G   A   Em

And I let it all out in mind_ that I'm not the on-ly per-son with these things in mind._

fused.)   (In-side of

Bm   G   A   Em

But all the va-can-cy. the words re-vealed_is the on-ly real thing_ that I've got left to feel._

me.)   (Noth-ing to

w/Fill 1 *(Elec. Gtr. 2)*

Bm   G   A   Em

Just stuck, hol-low and a-lone,_ and the fault___ is my own,_ and the fault_ is my own._ I want to

lose.)

𝄋 *Chorus:*

w/Rhy. Fig. 2 *(Elec. Gtr. 2) 1st 2 meas. only, 2 times*

B5   D5   G5   E5

heal,   I want to feel   what I thought was nev-er real._   I want to

Elec. Gtr. 2

f

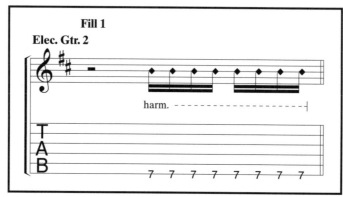

Fill 1

Elec. Gtr. 2

harm. -

15

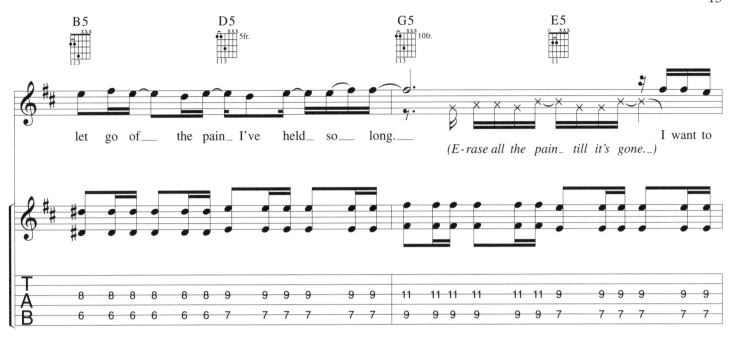

let go of__ the pain_ I've held_ so__ long.__

(E-rase all the pain_ till it's gone._)

I want to

w/Rhy. Fig. 2 *(Elec. Gtr. 2)*

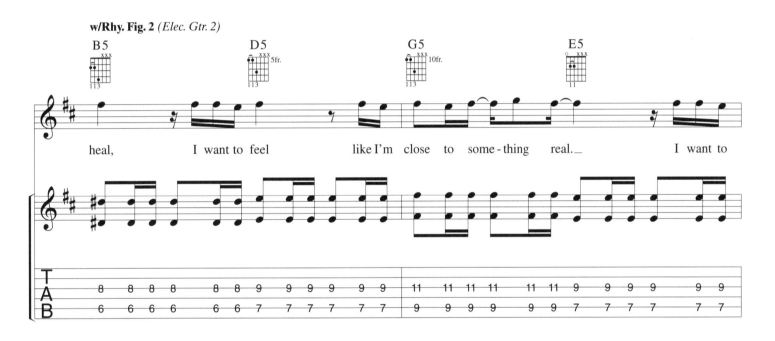

heal, I want to feel like I'm close to some-thing real.__ I want to

To Coda I ⊕
To Coda II ⊕⊕

find some-thing_ I've want-ed all__ a - long,__ some-where I__ be-long.

Verse 2:

And I've got noth-in' to say,_ I can't be-lieve I did-n't fall right down on my face._
(I was con-

Look-in' ev-'ry-where on-ly to find_ that it's not the way I had i-mag-ined it all in my mind._
fused.)
(So what am

What do I have but neg-a-tiv-i-ty,_'cause I can't jus-ti-fy the way ev-'ry-one is look-ing at me._
I?)
(Noth-ing to

Noth-ing to gain, hol-low and a-lone_ and the fault__ is my own,_ and the fault_ is my own._
lose.)
I want to

an - y - thing till I break a - way from me.___ I will break a - way I'll

D.S. % al Coda II

w/Fill 3 *(Elec. Gtr. 2)*

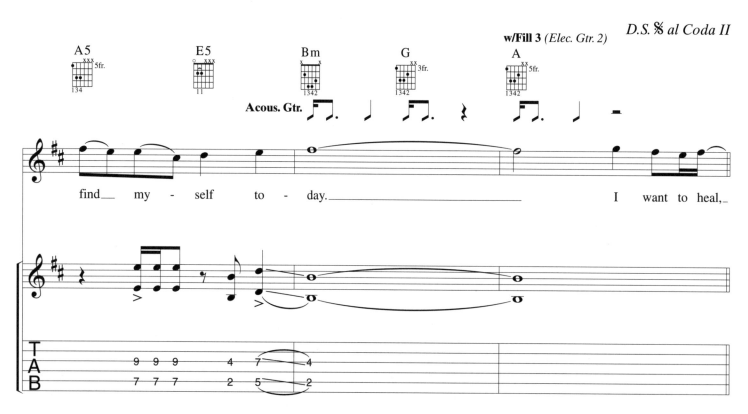

find___ my - self to - day._____ I want to heal,_

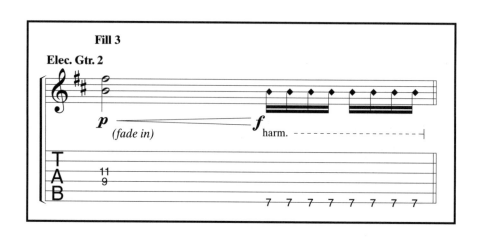

Fill 3

Elec. Gtr. 2

p _____ *f*
(fade in) harm. - - - - - - - - - - - - - - - - - - |

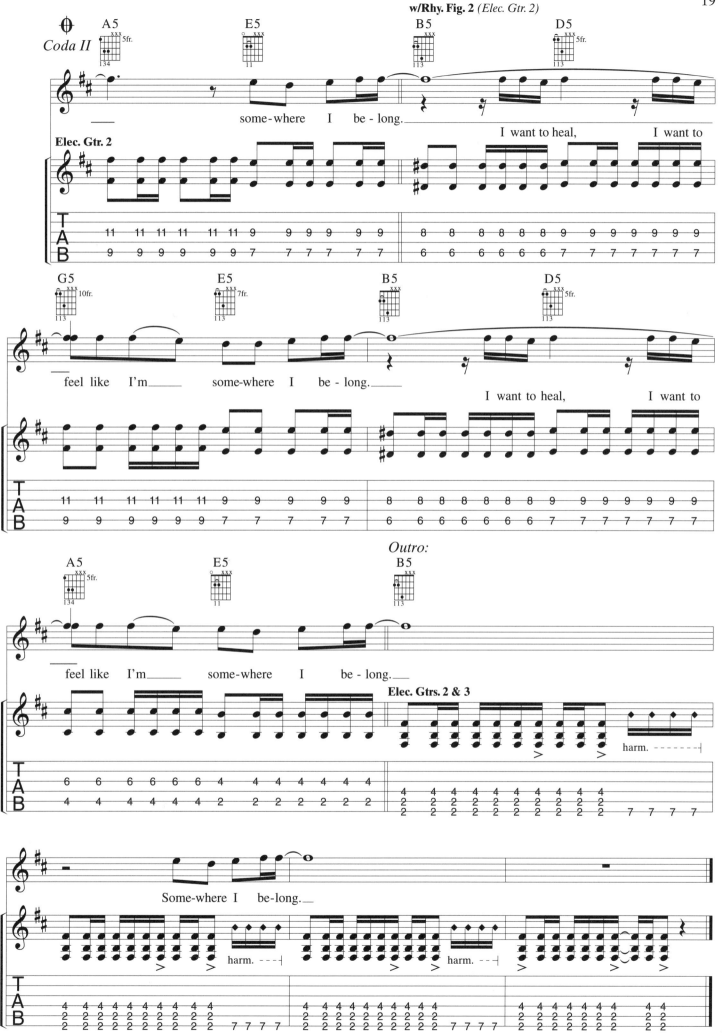

LYING FROM YOU

By LINKIN PARK

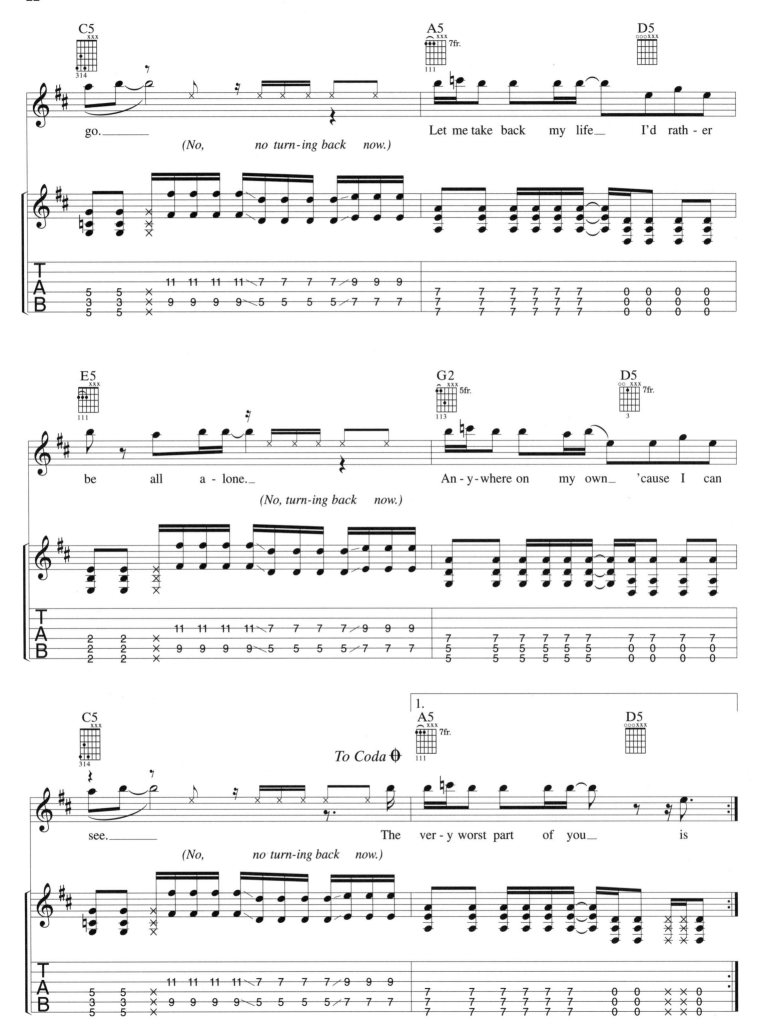

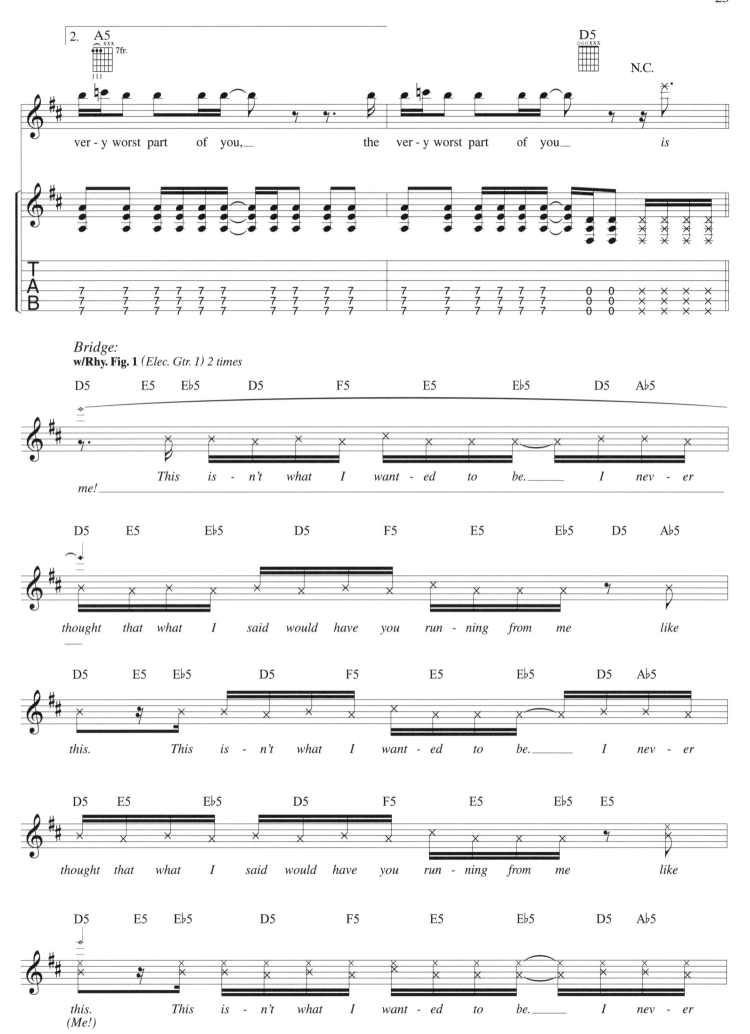

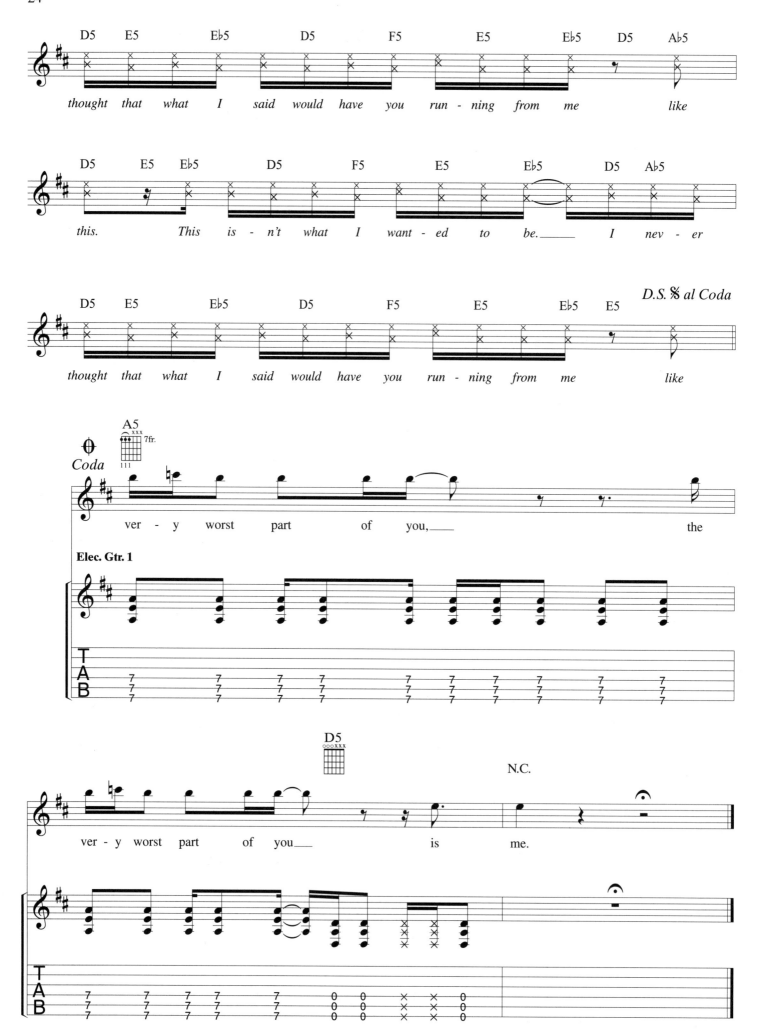

HIT THE FLOOR

By LINKIN PARK

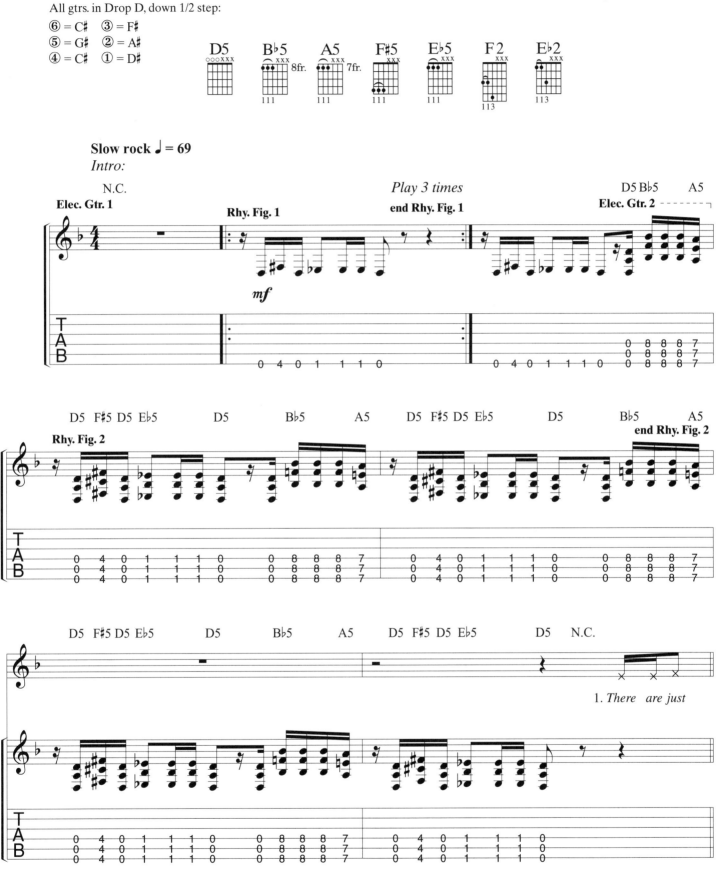

Verses 1 & 2:
w/Rhy. Fig. 1 *(Elec. Gtrs. 1) 8 times*

N.C.

too   man - y   times   that   peo - ple   have   tried   to   look   in - side   of   me,
2. *So   man - y   peo - ple   like   me   put   so   much   trust   in   all   your   lies,*

won - der - ing   what   I   think   of   you   and   I   pro - tect   you   out   of   cour - te - sy.
so   con - cerned   with   what   you   think   to   just   say   what   we   feel   in - side.

Too   man - y   times   that   I've   held   on   when   I   need - ed   to   push   a - way,   a -
So   man - y   peo - ple   like   me   walk   on   egg - shells   all   day   long.

fraid   to   say   what was   on   my   mind   a - fraid   to   say   what   I   need   to   say.
All   I   know   is   that   all   I   want   is   to   feel   like   I'm   not   stepped   on.   There   are

Too   man - y   things   that   you've   said   a - bout   me   when   I'm   not   a - round,
so   man - y   things   you   say   that   make   me   feel   you   crossed   the   line.

you   think   hav - ing   the   up - per   hand   means   you've   got   to   keep   put - ting   me   down.   But   I've   had
What   goes   up   will   sure - ly   fall   and   I'm   count - ing   down   the   time.   'Cause   I've   had

too   man - y   stand - offs   with   you,   it's   a - bout   as   much   as   I   can   stand.   So,   I'm
so   man - y   stand - offs   with   you,   it's   a - bout   as   much   as   I   can   stand.   So,   I'm

D5   Bb5   A5

**Elec.
Gtr. 2**

wait - ing   un - til   the   up - per   hand   is   mine.
wait - ing   un - til   the   up - per   hand   is   mine.

One   min - ute   you're   on

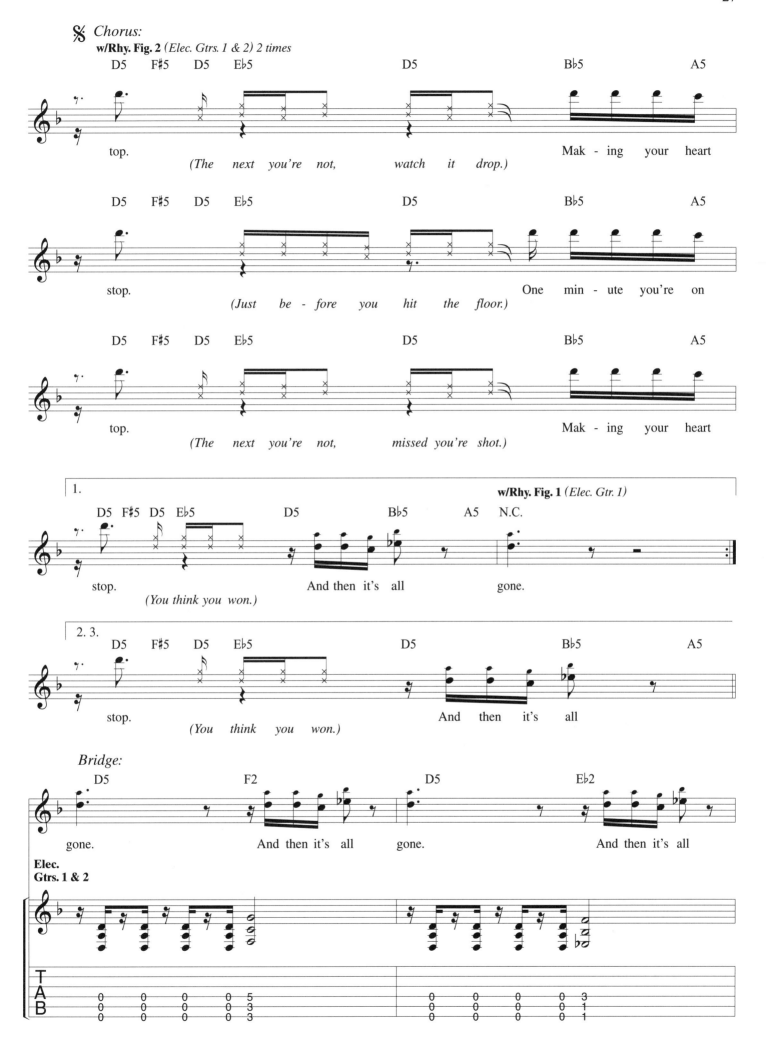

28

EASIER TO RUN

By LINKIN PARK

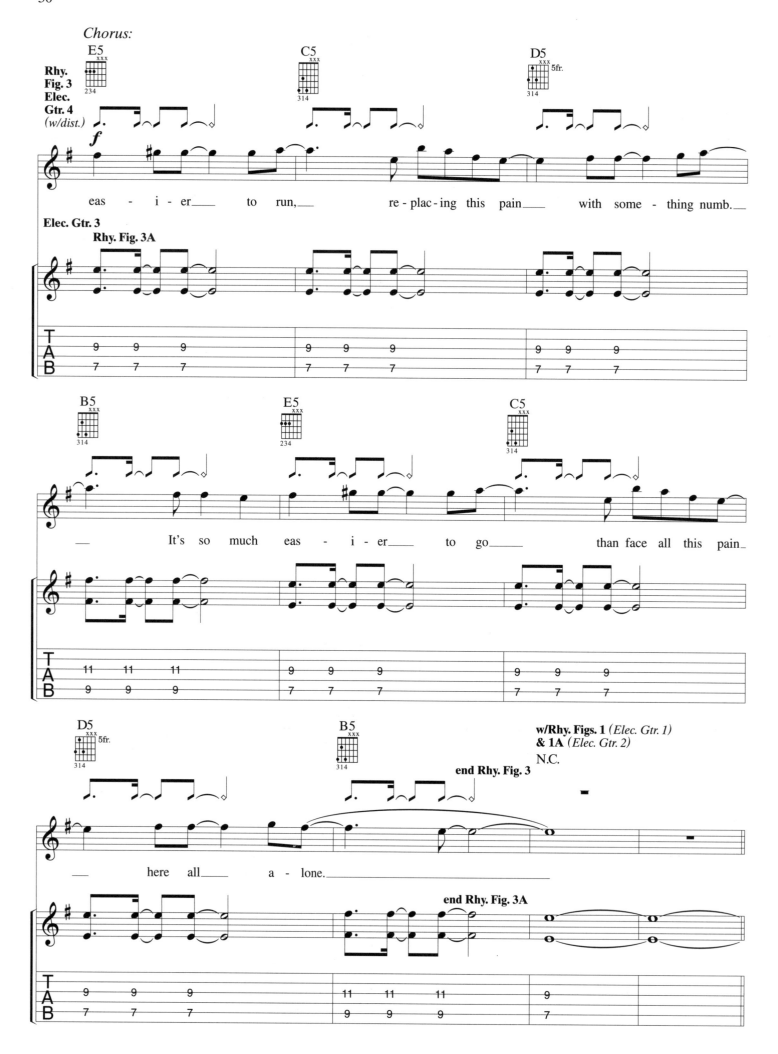

Verse 1:
w/Rhy. Figs. 1 *(Elec. Gtr. 1)* **& 1A** *(Elec. Gtr. 2) both 7 times*

Some-thing has been ta - ken from deep in - side of___ me. A se - cret I've kept locked a - way,___ no

one can ev - er see.___ Wounds so deep they nev-er show,___ they nev - er go a - way.___ Like

mov - ing pic - tures in my head,___ for years and years they've___ played._____ (If I could

change I would,___ take back the pain I would,___ re - trace

ev - 'ry wrong move that I made I would.___ If I coud

stand up and take the blame I would,___ if I could

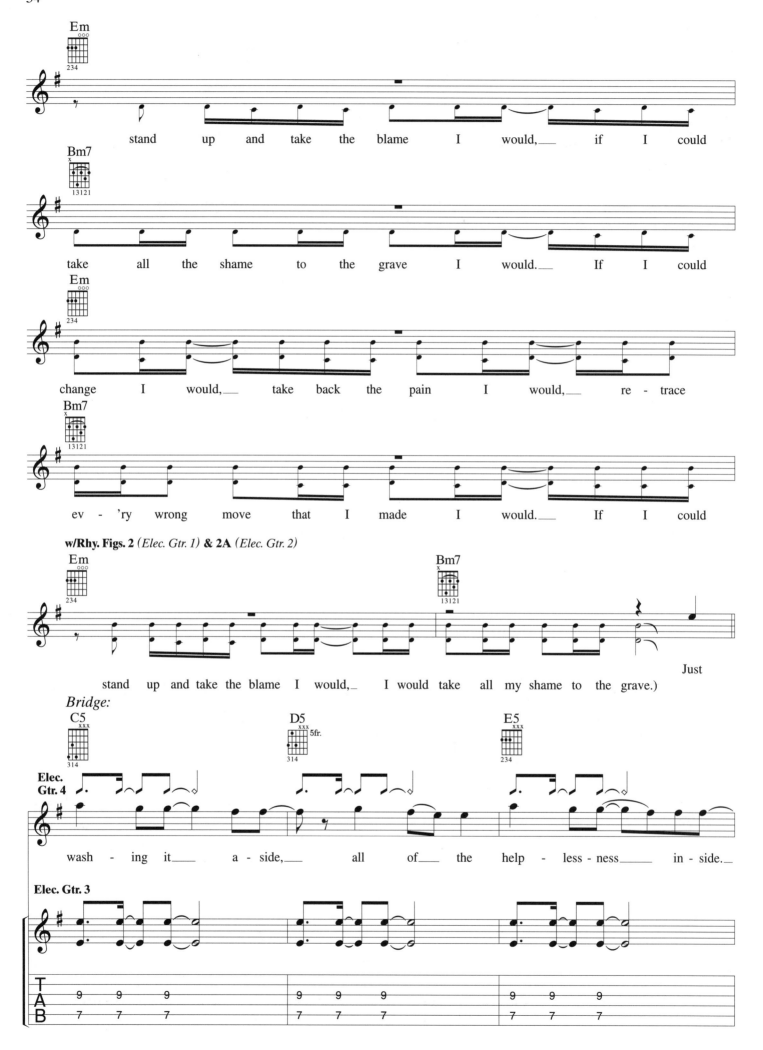

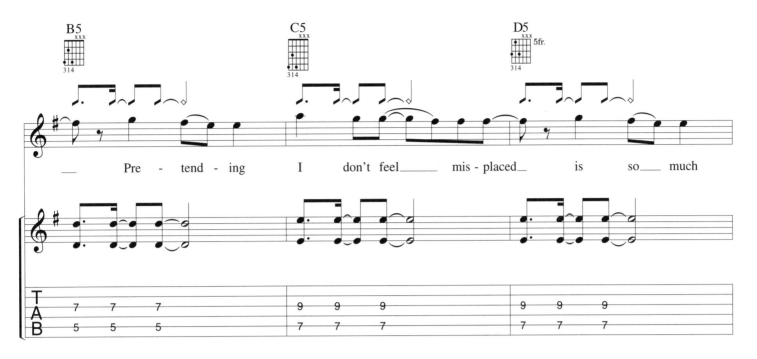

Pre-tend-ing I don't feel_____ mis-placed____ is so____ much

D.S. 𝄋 al Coda

sim - pl - er_____ than change.___ It's

w/Rhy. Figs. 3 *(Elec. Gtr. 3)* **& 3A** *(Elec. Gtr. 4)*

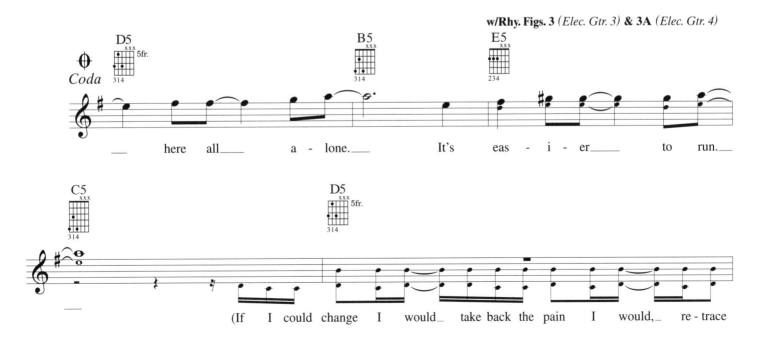

___ here all____ a - lone.___ It's eas - i - er_____ to run.___

(If I could change I would__ take back the pain I would,__ re - trace

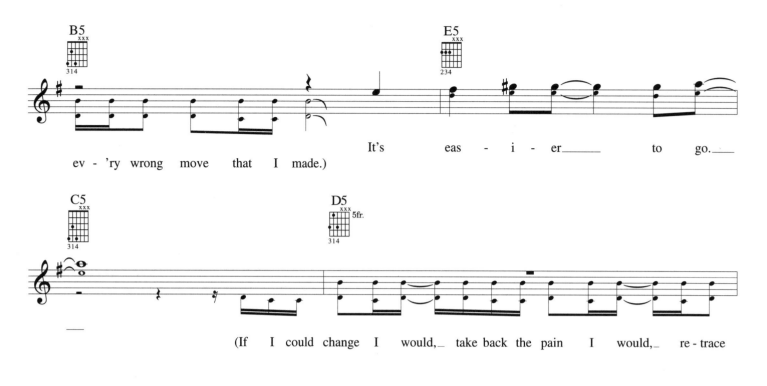

ev - 'ry wrong move that I made.)   It's   eas - i - er_____ to go.____

(If   I could change I   would,_ take back the pain   I   would,_   re - trace

ev - 'ry   wrong   move   that   I   made   I   would.___ If   I   could

stand   up and take the blame   I would,_   I would take all my shame   to the grave.)

FAINT

By LINKIN PARK

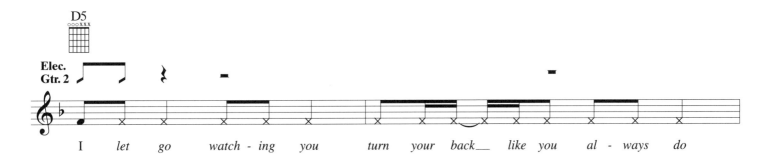

I let go watch - ing you turn your back___ like you al - ways do

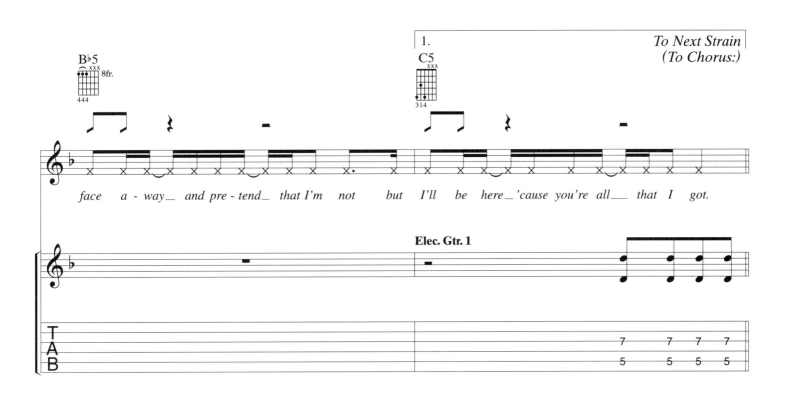

face a - way___ and pre - tend___ that I'm not but I'll be here___ 'cause you're all___ that I got.

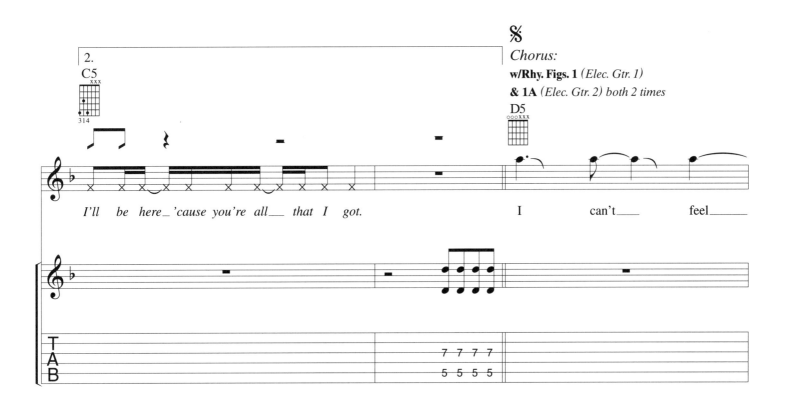

I'll be here___ 'cause you're all___ that I got. I can't___ feel___

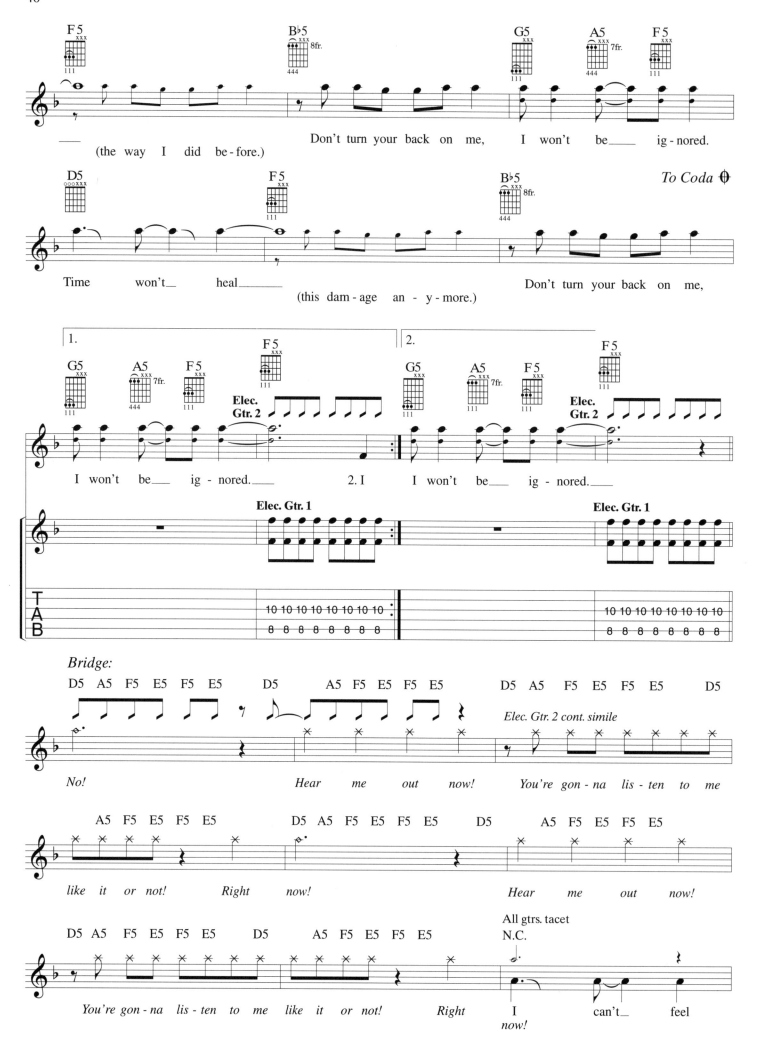

FIGURE.09

By LINKIN PARK

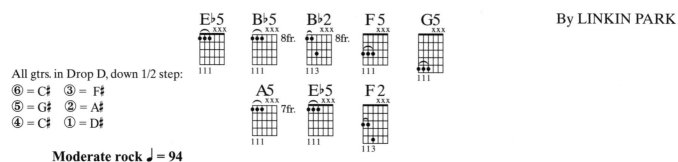

All gtrs. in Drop D, down 1/2 step:
⑥ = C♯ ③ = F♯
⑤ = G♯ ② = A♯
④ = C♯ ① = D♯

Moderate rock ♩ = 94

Intro:

N.C.

Elec. Gtr. 1 *(+ octave pedal)*

Riff A

*w/miscellaneous samples.
+ Set one octave lower.

Elec. Gtr. 1

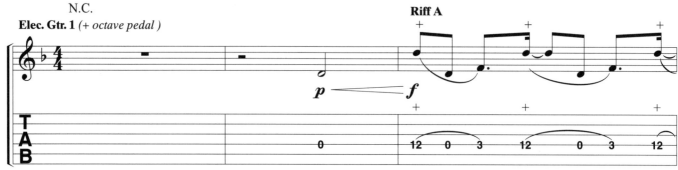

*Tap and slide w/RH.

Elec. Gtr. 1 tacet

D5 E♭5   D5 E♭5 D5   F2   D5   F2   D5

end Riff A

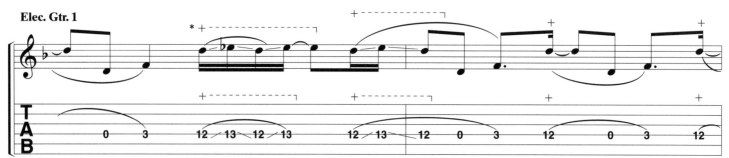

Elec. Gtr. 2

Rhy. Fig. 1

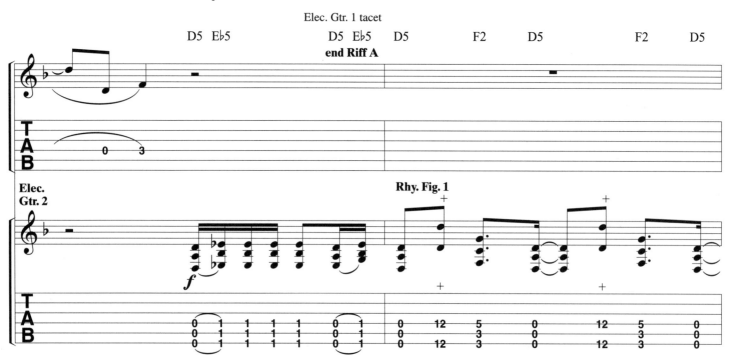

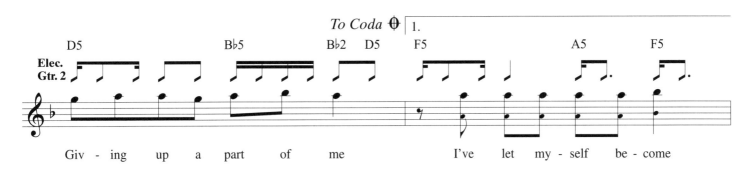

Giv - ing up a part of me I've let my - self be - come

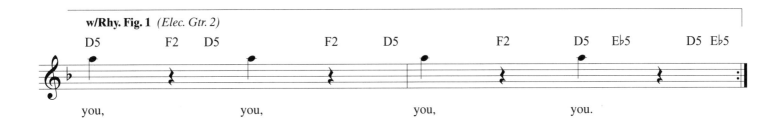

you, you, you, you.

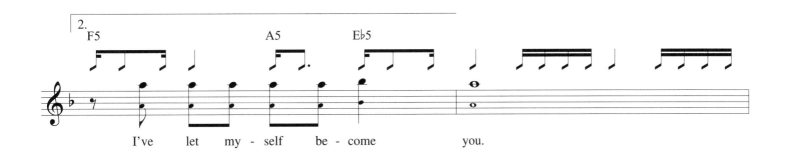

I've let my - self be - come you.

(Whispered:) It nev - er goes a - way. It nev - er goes a - way.

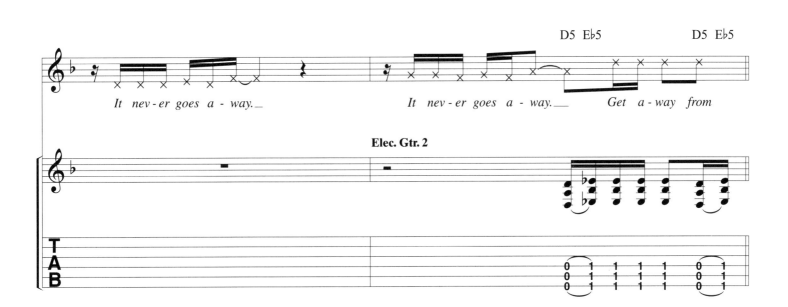

It nev - er goes a - way. It nev - er goes a - way. Get a - way from

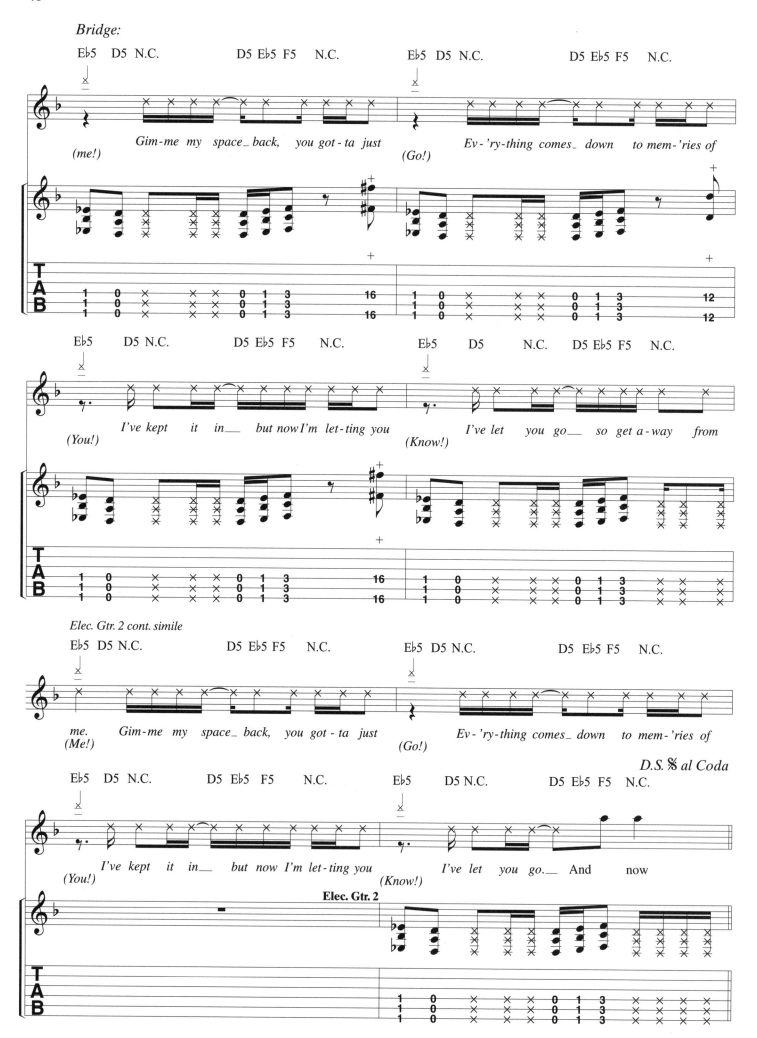

47

Coda

Outro:
w/Rhy. Fig. 2 *(Elec. Gtr. 2) 3 times*

I've let my - self be - come you.

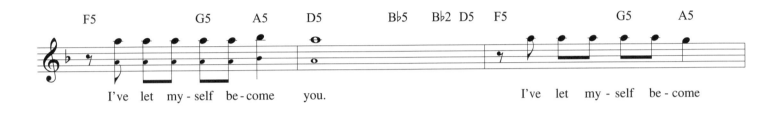

I've let my - self be - come you. I've let my - self be - come

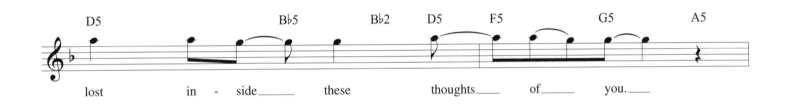

lost in - side____ these thoughts____ of____ you.____

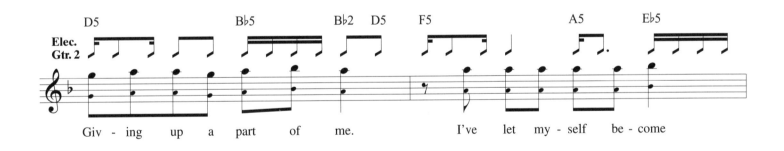

Giv - ing up a part of me. I've let my - self be - come

you.

BREAKING THE HABIT

By LINKIN PARK

Pre-chorus:
Keybd. & Elec. Gtr. 1 cont. simile

Chorus:
Keybd. cont. simile

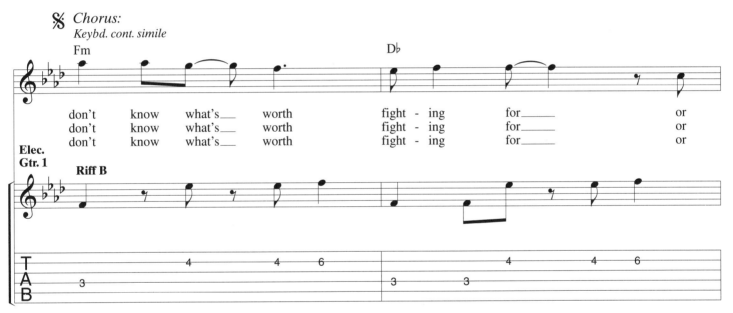

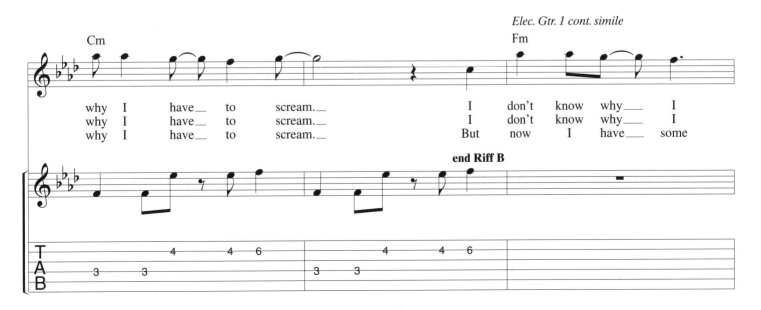

I'll nev - er fight___ a - gain.___

D.S. 𝄋 al Coda

And this is how___ it ends.___ 3. I

Coda

w/Riff B *(Elec. Gtr. 1)*

it, I'm break - ing___ the

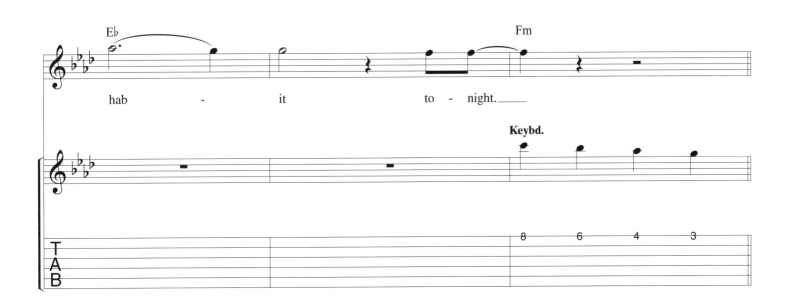

hab - it to - night.___

Keybd.

N.C.

Play 11 times

Elec.
Gtr. 2
(w/dist.)

p ———————— *f*

fdbk.

FROM THE INSIDE

By LINKIN PARK

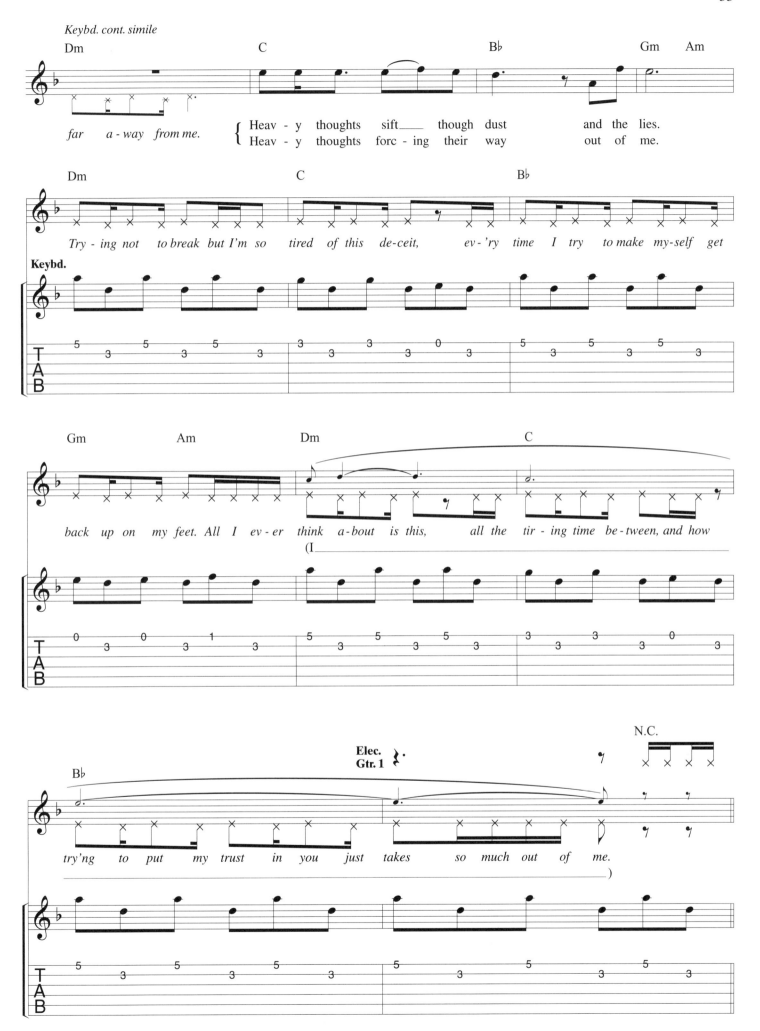

D.S. 𝄉 *al Coda*

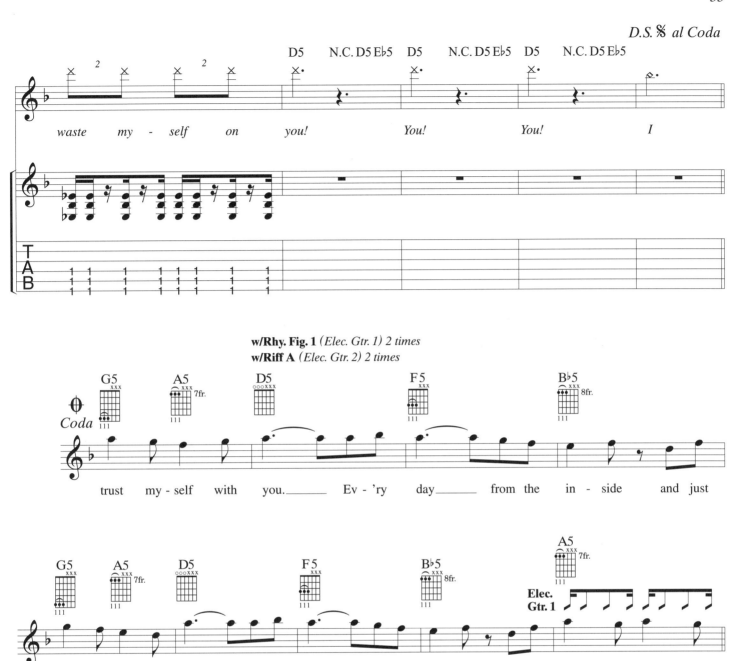

waste my - self on you! You! You! I

trust my - self with you.____ Ev - 'ry day____ from the in - side and just

throw it all a - way____ 'cause I swear____ for the last time I won't trust my - self with

you. You. You.

NOBODY'S LISTENING

By LINKIN PARK

All gtrs. in Drop D, down 1 1/2 steps:

⑥ = B   ③ = E
⑤ = F♯   ② = G♯
④ = B   ① = C♯

Moderately ♩ = 98

Intro:

*F5

*Implied harmony throughout.

**C-c - c - c - coming at you, coming at you, come, coming at you.
**Sampled vocals.

Yo.

Verses 1 & 2:

F5

1. Peep the style and the kids check-ing for it, the num-ber one ques-tion is how__ could you ig-nore it? We
heart full of pain, head full of stress, hand - ful of an-ger held in my chest.

drop right back in the cut o - ver base - ment tracks__ with raps that got you back-ing this up__ like re-
And ev-'ry thing left's a waste of time I hate my___ rhymes but hate ev-'ry-one els - es more._ I'm

wind that. We're just roll - ing with the rhy - thm, rise from the ash-es of sty-lis-tic di - vi-sion with
rid-ing on the back of this pres - sure guess-ing that it's bet-ter I can't keep my-self to-geth-er be-cause

these non - stop lyr - ics of life liv - ing not to be for-got - ten but still__ un - for-giv-en.
all of this stress gave me some-thing to write on, the pain gave me some-thing I could set my sights on.

But in the mean - time there are those__ who wan-na talk this and that, so__ I sup-pose that it
You nev-er for-get the blood, sweat and tears, the up - hill strug-gle o - ver years, the fear and

gets to a point where feel-ings got to get hurt and get dirt-y with the peo-ple spread-ing the dirt,_ it goes. }
trash talk - ing and the peo-ple it was to and the peo-ple that start-ed it just like you. }

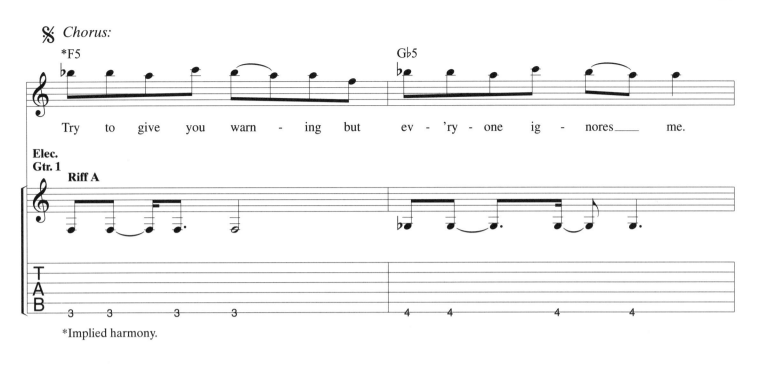

*Implied harmony.

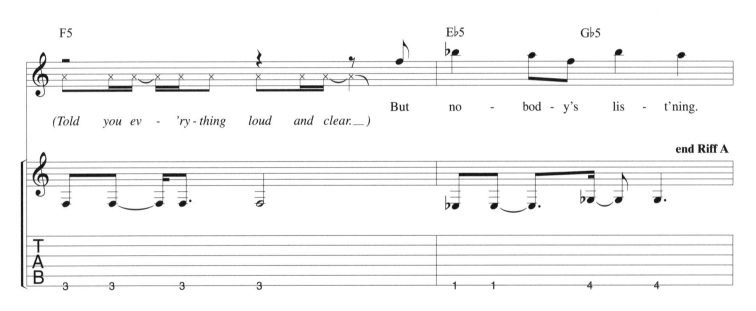

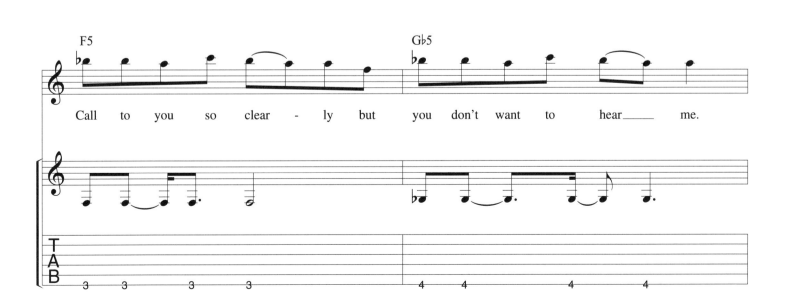

SESSION

All gtrs. in Drop D, down 1/2 step:
⑥ = C♯ ③ = F♯
⑤ = G♯ ② = A♯
④ = C♯ ① = D♯

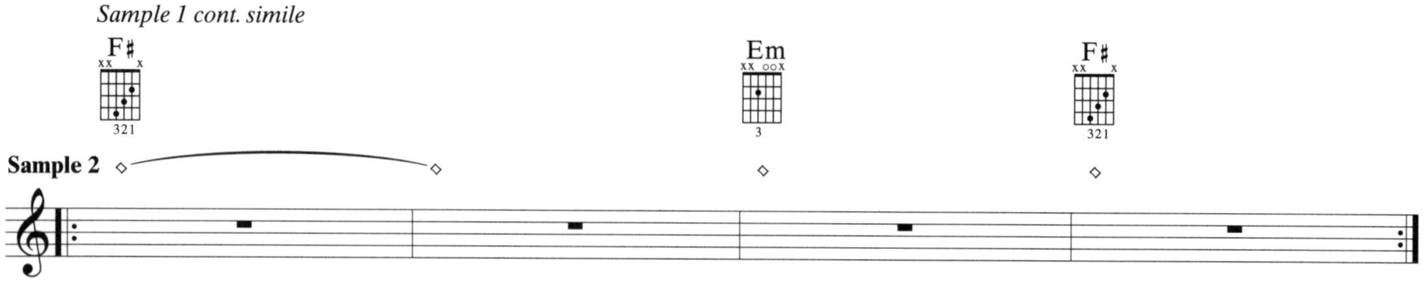

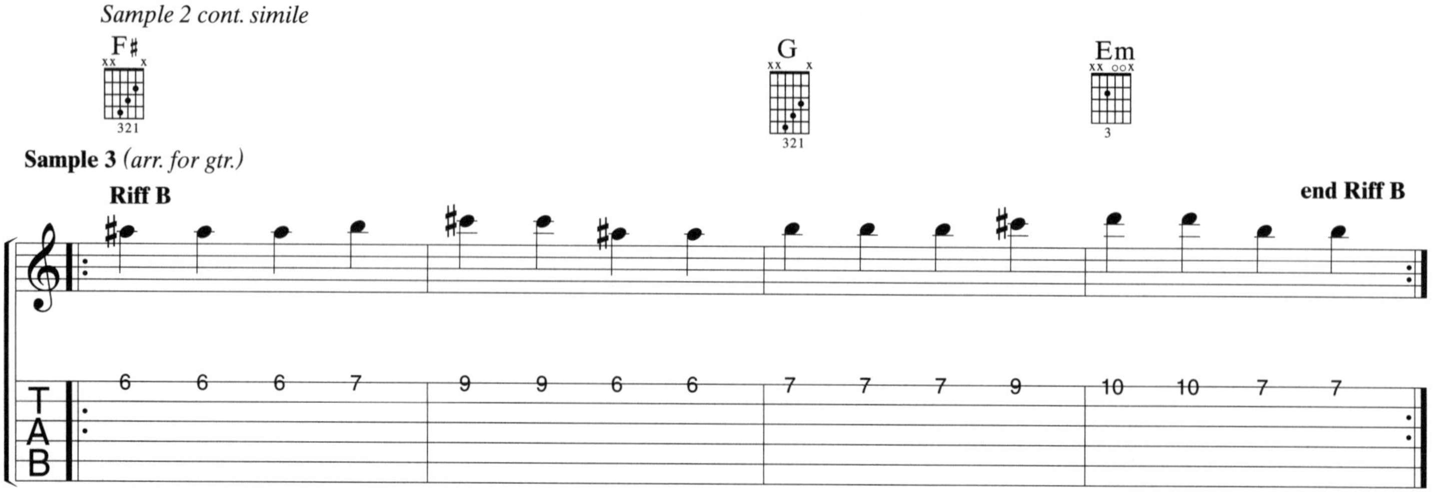

By LINKIN PARK

Moderately ♩ = 94

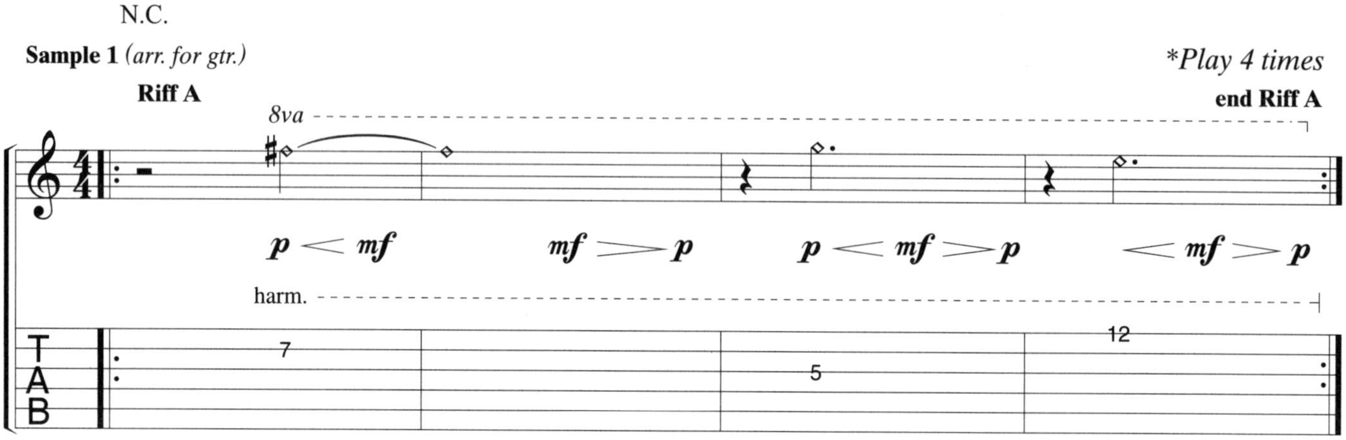

N.C.
Sample 1 (arr. for gtr.)
*Play 4 times
Riff A
end Riff A
8va
p < mf
mf > p
p < mf > p
< mf > p
harm.
T
A
B
7
5
12

*Drums enter third time.

Sample 1 cont. simile
F♯
321
Em
3
F♯
321
Sample 2

Sample 2 cont. simile
F♯
321
G
321
Em
3
Sample 3 (arr. for gtr.)
Riff B
end Riff B
T
A
B
6 6 6 7
9 9 6 6
7 7 7 9
10 10 7 7

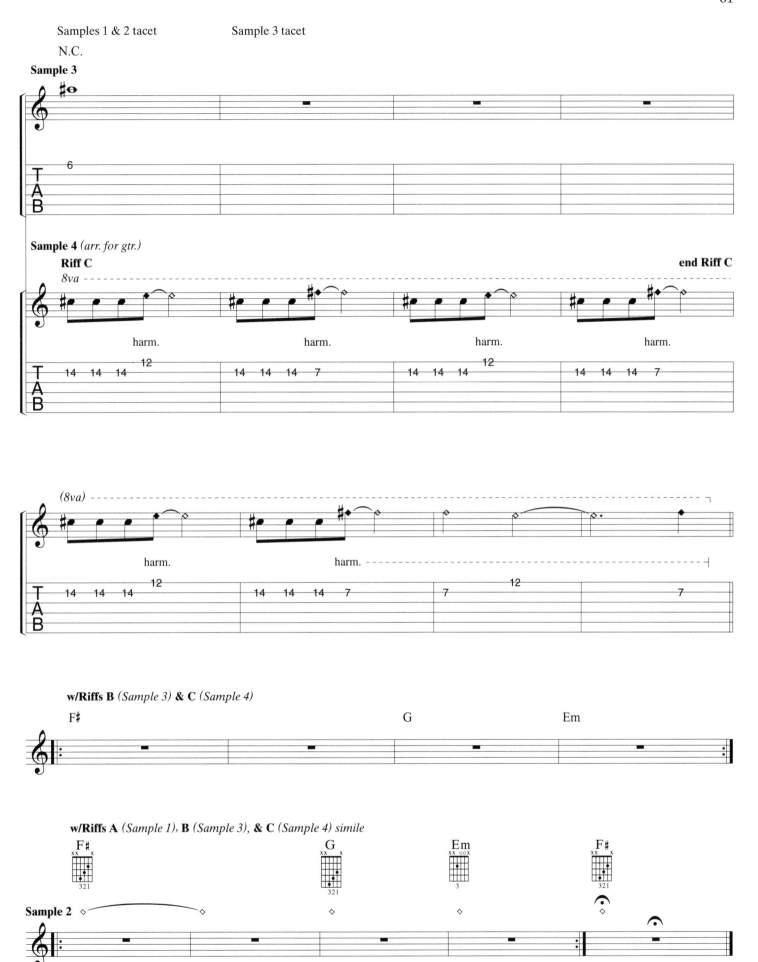

NUMB

By LINKIN PARK

All gtrs. in Drop D, down 1/2 step:

⑥ = C♯ ③ = F♯
⑤ = G♯ ② = A♯
④ = C♯ ① = D♯

Moderately ♩ = 108

Intro:

N.C.

© 2003 Zomba Songs Inc. (BMI)/ Chesterchaz Publishing (BMI)/ Big Bad Mr. Hahn Music (BMI)/
Nondisclosure Agreement Music (BMI)/ Rob Bourdon Music (BMI)/
Kenji Kobayashi Music (BMI)/ Pancakey Cakes Music (BMI)
All Rights on behalf of Chesterchaz Publishing (BMI)/ Big Bad Mr. Hahn Music (BMI)/
Nondisclosure Agreement Music (BMI)/ Rob Bourdon Music (BMI)/ Kenji Kobayashi Music (BMI)/
Pancakey Cakes Music (BMI) Administered by Zomba Songs Inc. (BMI)
All Rights Reserved

Verse 1:

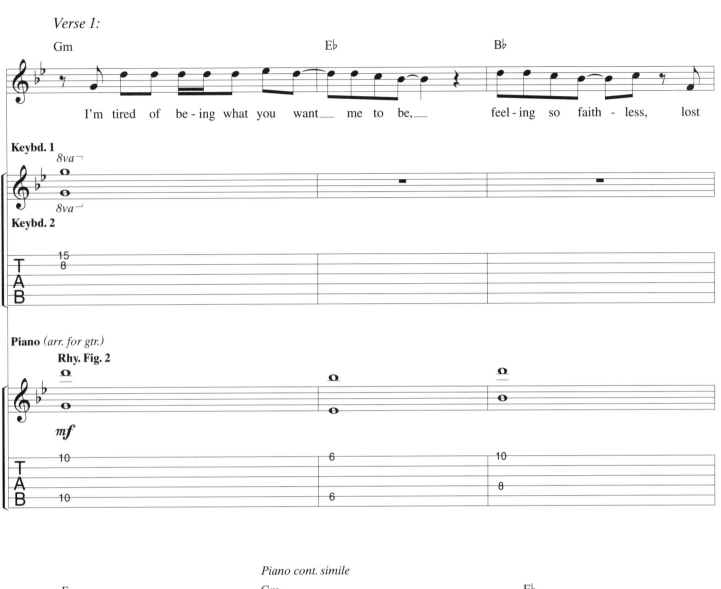

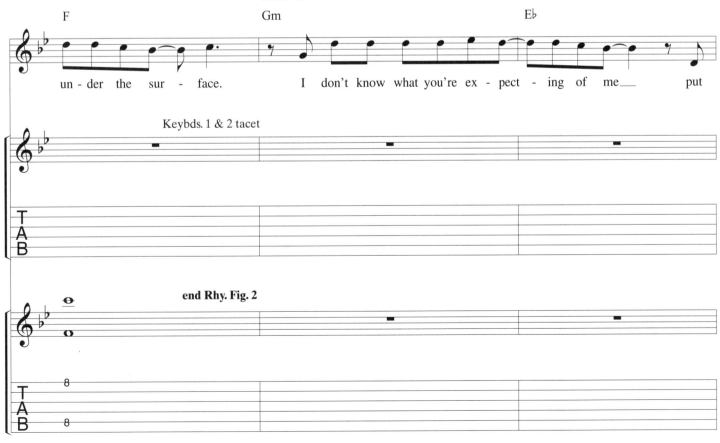

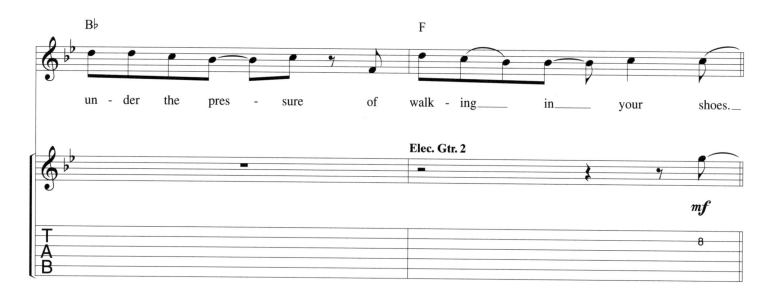

un - der the pres - sure of walk - ing_____ in_____ your shoes._

Elec. Gtr. 2

mf

Pre-chorus 1:

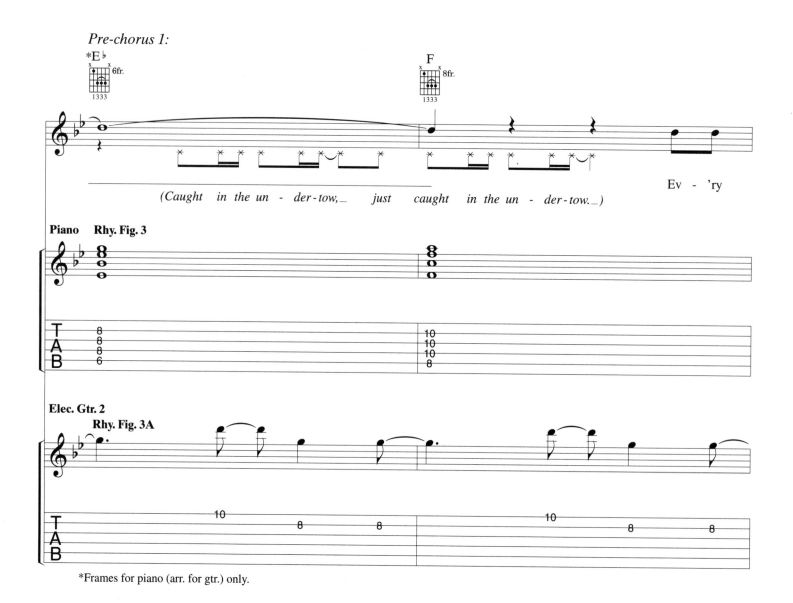

(Caught in the un - der - tow,_ just caught in the un - der - tow._) Ev - 'ry

Piano Rhy. Fig. 3

Elec. Gtr. 2

Rhy. Fig. 3A

*Frames for piano (arr. for gtr.) only.

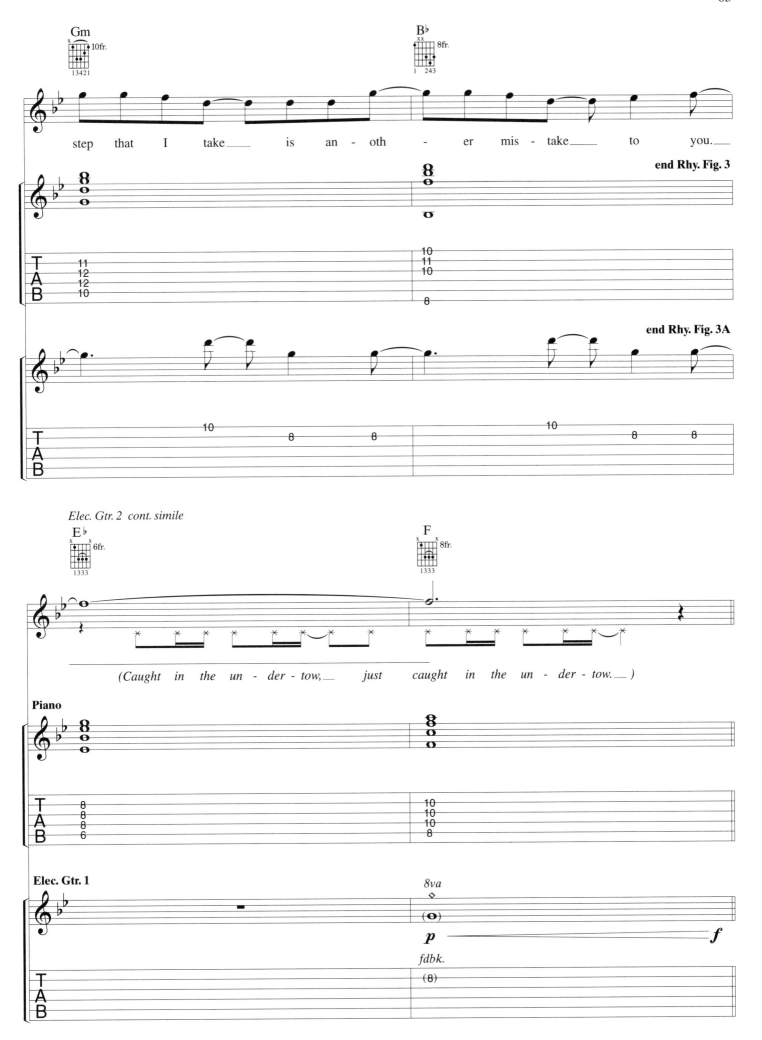

step that I take___ is an - oth - er mis - take___ to you.___

end Rhy. Fig. 3

end Rhy. Fig. 3A

Elec. Gtr. 2 cont. simile

(Caught in the un - der - tow,___ just caught in the un - der - tow. ___)

Piano

Elec. Gtr. 1

8va

p ———————— *f*

fdbk.

Pre-chorus 2:
w/Rhy. Figs. 3 *(Piano)* **& 3A** *(Elec. Gtr. 2) both 2 times*

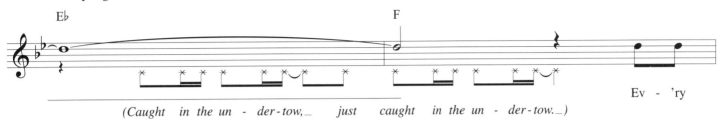

(Caught in the un - der - tow, __ just caught in the un - der - tow. __)

Ev - 'ry

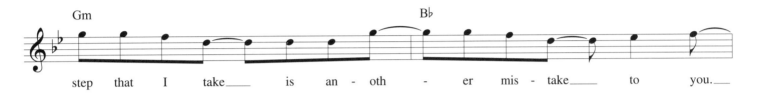

step that I take __ is an - oth - er mis - take __ to you. __

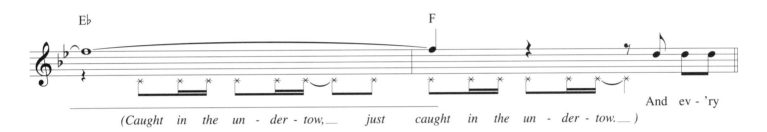

(Caught in the un - der - tow, __ just caught in the un - der - tow. __)

And ev - 'ry

Chorus:
w/Rhy. Figs. 1 *(Elec. Gtr. 1)* **& 1A** *(Keybd. 2)*

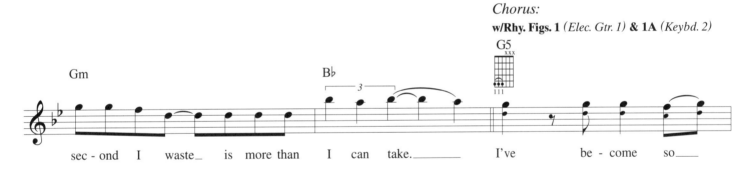

sec - ond I waste __ is more than I can take. __ I've be - come so __

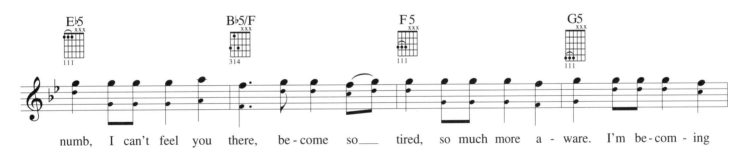

numb, I can't feel you there, be - come so __ tired, so much more a - ware. I'm be - com - ing

Bridge:
w/Rhy. Fig. 1A *(Keybd. 2)*
1 1/2 times

this, all I want to do is be more like me and be less like you. And I know __

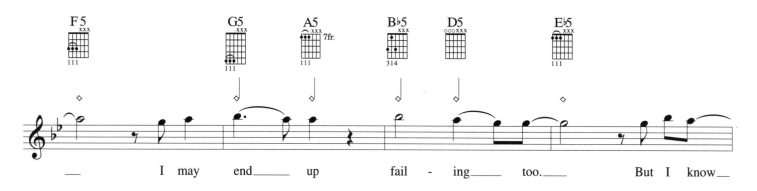

I may end___ up fail - ing___ too.___ But I know___

___ you were just like_ me___ with some-one dis - ap - point - ed in you._

D.S. % al Coda

___

me and be less like

w/Rhy. Figs. 1 *(Elec. Gtr. 1)* & 1A *(Keybd. 2) both 2 times*
w/Riff A *(Keybd. 1) 2 times*

I've be - come so_____ numb._____
(you.)
(I can't feel you

there.)
(I'm tired of be - ing what you want___ me to be._____)

I've be - come so_____ numb._____
(I can't feel you

there.)
(I'm tired of be - ing what you want___ me to be._____)

Band tacet

N.C.

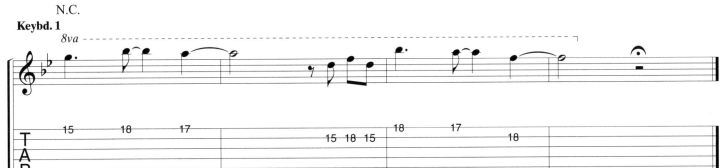

ALSO AVAILABLE